JUST IN T
OF TIME!
(a Detective Red Mistletoe mystery)

By
LINDA DAUGHERTY

Dramatic Publishing
Woodstock, Illinois • England • Australia • New Zealand

This play is dedicated
to
Ada Lynn
wife, mother, grandmother, actress, comedian,
vaudevillian and friend

IMPORTANT BILLING AND CREDIT REQUIREMENTS

All producers of the play *must* give credit to the author of the play in all programs distributed in connection with performances of the play and in all instances in which the title of the play appears for purposes of advertising, publicizing or otherwise exploiting the play and/or a production. The name of the author *must* also appear on a separate line, on which no other name appears, immediately following the title, and *must* appear in size of type not less than fifty percent (50%) the size of the title type. Biographical information on the author, if included in the playbook, may be used in all programs. *In all programs this notice must appear:*

"Produced by special arrangement with
THE DRAMATIC PUBLISHING COMPANY of Woodstock, Illinois"

Just in the Nick of Time! premiered at the Dallas Children's Theater (Robyn Flatt, Executive Artistic Director) on December 1, 1994, directed by Andre du Broc.

ORIGINAL CAST

Red Mistletoe	Karl Schaeffer
Fruitcake	Eric B. Knapp
Mrs. Claus	Ada Lynn*
Doc Green	Gavin Perry
Holly	Brigitte Bavousett
Mr. Claus	As Himself

		GOLD CAST	**SILVER CAST**
Elves: Captain		Morgan Feldman	Melissa Box
		Brent Black	Pete Camp
		Colin Malone	Jeffrey Miller
		Dru Ransom	Sandy Park
Gumdrops:	Green	Danielle Davenport	Kawana Anderson
	Red	Karrah Black	Danielle Sherwood
	Purple	Jordan Brooks	Sally Rodgers
Toy Testers		John Harden	Jake Speck
		Robert Harden	Jon Greer
Snowflakes		Dara Ransom	Elizabeth Kusin
		Claire Jordan	Joy Camp
Candy Cane		Emily Vardell	Marti Ethridge
Christmas Tree		Jeff Fijolek	Caroline Kusin

ORIGINAL PRODUCTION STAFF

Light Design	Zak Herring
Set Design	Yoichi and Katie Aoki
Costume Design	Mary Therese D'Avignon
Props Design	David Fisher
Sound Design	Andre du Broc
Production Manager	Darren Brannon
Production Sponsor	The Rosewood Corporation

*Member Actors' Equity Association.

JUST IN THE NICK OF TIME!
(a Detective Red Mistletoe mystery)

A Play in Two Acts
For 3m., 2w., 2 m. or w., 13+ children/teens

CHARACTERS (in order of appearance)

RED MISTLETOE . . . . Hard-boiled Bogart/Columbo-type
detective. Wears a red trench coat and hat.

GIRL ELVES #1, #2 and #3 . . . . Teenagers. Energetic,
enthusiastic, boy crazy.

TOY TESTER ELVES #1, #2 and #3 . . . . Tough, athletic,
girls or boys.

ELDER ELVES #1 and #2 . . . . The older generation,
children or teens

FRUITCAKE (VENDOR) (m or w) . . . . . . Humbug's sidekick.
Not too bright.

DOCTOR GREEN (m or w) . . . . Doctor at North Pole
(for people and animals). Wears a green coat.

MRS. CLAUS . . . Santa's wife. Kind, sweet, a bit disorganized.

ORANGE GUMDROP . . . . Child, 5 to 10 years old.

PURPLE GUMDROP . . . . Child, 5 to 10 years old.

SNOWFLAKE . . . . Girl, 8 to 12 years old.

CANDY CANE . . . . Child, 8 to 12 years old.

TREE . . . . Child or Teenager.

BOB HUMBUG . . . Nasty and ill-humored. Dressed as Scrooge in nightshirt and cap.

HOLLY WREATH. . . Humbug's attractive assistant. A redhead in green dress with large round wreath-like collar.

SANTA CLAUS. . . . . Himself.

NOTES: Additional roles for children and teens may be added: Snowflakes, Candy Canes, Elves, Trees and various colored Gumdrops.

This play contains a special effect by which all or selected sets, costumes and actors are transformed from their normal full color to the tones of a black-and-white movie. The effect is produced by changing costumes, actors' makeup and sets to black, white and shades of gray and lighting without gels. After Santa Claus disappears shortly before the end of Act I, there are hints of what is to come in the form of Holly's black lipstick, Doctor Green's fading costume and Orange and Purple Gumdrops' total transformation into black and white. Act II opens totally in black and white and returns to color upon Santa Claus' reappearance at the end of the play. The following characters are transformed into black and white:

Red Mistletoe
Mrs. Claus
Humbug
Holly
Fruitcake
Elder Elf #1
Elder Elf #2
Doctor Green
Orange Gumdrop
Purple Gumdrop
Snowflake
Tree
Candy Cane

ACT I

(A spotlight shines down in the darkness. Detective RED MISTLETOE, dressed in a red hat and red trench coat with turned-up collar, walks into the light.)

RED. It was cold that Christmas. I was frozen to the bone. My feet—blocks of ice. My teeth—chattering an S.O.S. It was as cold a Christmas as I could remember. How cold was it? It was so cold the icicles had icicles. *It was cold!* But that's the way we like it up north, up where Santa lives. It's a quiet town—the North Pole—most of the year. Except those few weeks before Christmas. Hey, I don't have to tell you that. But I'm getting ahead of myself, putting the sleigh before the reindeer. I'm Red Mistletoe, detective. It's my job to make sure everything runs smoothly up at the North Pole. Our story begins way back in September—way before the Christmas rush. But, of course, at the North Pole, it's always snowing and those colorful Christmas decorations are up year 'round. So September looks *exactly* like December. Just quieter, slower. It was the middle of September—a nice, quiet, average Tuesday—not the kind of day you'd expect a mystery to begin.

(RED walks out of spotlight. Lights rise on the North Pole—a charming, snowy village. A snow cone VENDOR pushes colorful cart down the street. Several cones of various flavors are displayed.)

VENDOR. Snow cones! Snow cones!

(ELF GIRLS #1, #2 and #3 enter, talking and giggling together.)

ELF GIRL #1. Oh, those gorgeous blue eyes of his! Tell us! What did he say?!
ELF GIRL #2. Tell us! You've got to tell us!
ELF GIRL #3 *(dramatically)*. He looked at me with those big *blue* eyes of his—

(ELF GIRLS squeal with delight.)

ELF GIRL #3 *(cont'd)*. And he said—he said—he's going to ask for a transfer—from radio-controlled toys!
ELF GIRL #2. What?!
ELF GIRL #1. You're kidding?!
ELF GIRL #3. He wants to transfer to—*Legos!*

(ELF GIRLS scream "Legos!!!" together in excitement.)

ELF GIRL #1. Do you know what this means? Blue eyes is crazy for you!
ELF GIRL #2. Oh, you're so lucky! All day long you'll be making Legos together and looking into his large, mysterious *baby-blue* eyes.

(They all sigh. VENDOR approaches.)

VENDOR. How about a snow cone?

ELF GIRL #1. No, thanks.

ELF GIRL #2. Not me.

ELF GIRL #3. Sure, I'll take one.

VENDOR. What flavor?

ELF GIRL #3 *(dreamily). Blue*-berry.

(ELF GIRLS scream and exit. TOY TESTER ELVES #1 and #2 enter. TOY TESTER ELF #1 is riding a skateboard and TOY TESTER ELF #2, bouncing on a pogo stick. [Popular seasonal toys may be substituted.])

TOY TESTER ELF #2 *(counting bounces).* 5,621, 5,622, 5,623...

TOY TESTER ELF #1 *(coming to a sudden stop and indicating skateboard).* Do you like this DayGlo orange color or should we stick with red?

TOY TESTER ELF #2 *(still bouncing).* 5,630, 5,631, 5,632...

TOY TESTER ELF #1. Will you take a break?! That pogo stick is indestructible!

(TOY TESTER ELF #2 stops jumping as TOY TESTER ELF #3 enters riding a scooter, circles the OTHERS and stops.)

TOY TESTER ELF #3. Great turns, excellent handling, good traction, two-wheel disk brakes, classy interior, great color.

TOY TESTER ELF #2. Nice scooter.

TOY TESTER #1. These toys are great. Come on. Let's go try out some new board games.

TOY TESTER #3. I love this job. Toy testing is so much fun. And to think I used to work in wrapping paper!

(TOY TESTER ELVES exit, rolling and bouncing. ELDER ELVES #1 and #2 enter with lunch boxes.)

ELDER ELF #1. Batteries, batteries, batteries. That's all they want. Electrified, motorized, flashing, whirring, beeping, buzzing. That's what these kids want today.

ELDER ELF #2. Maybe you and I are too old-fashioned.

ELDER ELF #1. Whatever happened to the wooden boat, the rubber-band racing car, the wind-up toy?

ELDER ELF #2. We've got to change with the times.

ELDER ELF #1. I remember a time when an orange or a peppermint was a special gift, a new pair of socks, a treat! Ah, those were the good old days. Who remembers?

ELDER ELF #2. The point's not the presents. The point is we still remember *Christmas*. Times change. People are rich or poor. But they still find a way to remember and celebrate Christmas.

ELDER ELF #1 *(change of heart)*. Oh, you're right, you're right. It's the *spirit* of the season that matters. *(He rubs his back.)*

ELDER ELF #2. Your lumbago acting up?

ELDER ELF #1. A bit. I should retire.

ELDER ELF #2. What? You'll be putting those video games together when you're 230!

(DOCTOR GREEN enters in a hurry, carrying medical bag.)

ELDER ELF #2. Hey, Doctor Green, what's the hurry?

VENDOR. How about a snow cone?

DOCTOR GREEN. No time!

ELDER ELF #1. Hey, Doctor, I've got this crick in the back.

DOCTOR GREEN. Sorry. Later. I've got a reindeer with a condition.

ELDER ELF #1. Cough?

ELDER ELF #2. Cold?

DOCTOR GREEN. No, motherhood!

(DOCTOR GREEN exits and rushes past the entering RED MISTLETOE.)

RED. Wow, Doctor Green's in a hurry. Anything amiss?

ELDER ELF #2. A blessed event at the reindeer barn.

(ELDER ELVES #1 and #2 exit.)

RED. Ah, well, that calls for a celebration. Give me a snow cone.

VENDOR. What flavor?

RED. Cherry.

(MRS. CLAUS enters, surrounded by SNOWFLAKE, CANDY CANE, TREE and PURPLE and ORANGE GUMDROPS. VENDOR gives snow cone to RED.)

SNOWFLAKE. May I have a grape snow cone, Mrs. Claus?

MRS. CLAUS. We can't have a purple Snowflake, dear. You may all have one after rehearsal. Come on, everyone. Stay together... Snowflake, Tree, Candy Cane. Come along!

RED. Hello, Mrs. Claus. How's rehearsal going?

MRS. CLAUS. Oh, Detective Mistletoe. I don't know. It's the dancing Tree I'm worried about. He [She] can't see where he's [she's] going in his [her] costume. And Santa always forgets rehearsal. Making lists and trying new toys. I wonder if this Christmas show was such a good idea.

RED. I'm sure it will be wonderful.

MRS. CLAUS. You'll come, won't you? It's going to be very colorful.

RED. Wouldn't miss it.

MRS. CLAUS. December 24th, six p.m. sharp.

RED. I'll be there.

MRS. CLAUS *(herding CHILDREN)*. This way, everyone. Do we have the Gumdrops?

PURPLE & ORANGE GUMDROPS. Present!

(MRS. CLAUS and CHILDREN exit.)

RED *(to VENDOR)*. You're new around these parts, aren't you?

VENDOR. Yeah, yeah—I'm new. I, uh, used to live, uh, uh, just north of the South Pole, but the weather, you know, too cold. I just relocated to, uh…just south of the North Pole.

RED. Just south of the North Pole? Interesting... Just one more thing. See many polar bears down south?

VENDOR. Polar bears?

RED. Yeah, polar bears. See many of those? Down south at the South Pole?

VENDOR. Uh...yeah, yeah, lots of polar bears at the South Pole. Always scaring off the customers.

RED. Hmm...well, see you around. *(RED exits, balancing his snow cone and writing in small notebook.)*

VENDOR. Yeah. See you around. *(VENDOR looks around, sees the coast is clear, picks up one of the snow cones and talks into it.)* Hello, boss? *(Tries another snow cone.)* Hello, boss? *(Tries another.)* Hello, boss?!

(VENDOR puts snow cone to ear. Lights up on HUM-BUG's house.)

HUMBUG *(shouting into phone)*. Fruitcake, where have you been?!

VENDOR *(who is FRUITCAKE in disguise, talks into snow cone.)*. Sorry, boss, but business has been booming. Who'd have thought anyone would want a snow cone at the North Pole?

HUMBUG. Have you seen him, Fruitcake?

VENDOR (FRUITCAKE). Him?

HUMBUG. Santa!

VENDOR (FRUITCAKE). No, no, not yet. But I will, boss, I will. Oh, and boss, Santa's looking for a secretary. I saw the notice on the bulletin board at the Cranberry Coffee Shop.

HUMBUG. Secretary? Interesting. Now find Santa and tail him.

VENDOR (FRUITCAKE). Tail Santa?

HUMBUG. *Follow* him, Fruitcake!

VENDOR (FRUITCAKE). Oh, yeah, boss, yeah. You can count on me.

(HUMBUG slams down phone. FRUITCAKE reacts. Lights out on FRUITCAKE at the North Pole.)

HUMBUG. What a *fruitcake!*

(HOLLY enters.)

HOLLY. Here's the mail, boss. *(HOLLY hands catalogues to HUMBUG as she reads addressee's names.)* Humbug—Humbug—Mr. B. Humbug—Occupant—The Lady of the House—

HUMBUG *(grabbing rest of the mail)*. Give me those! Catalogues—nothing but catalogues! It's only September and they've started again with the Christmas catalogues. *(Pacing.)* I've got to do something…I've got to do something…

HOLLY. Why don't you start an exercise program?

HUMBUG. That's not what I mean, Holly. I've got to do something about Christmas.

HOLLY. No kidding? Only ninety-eight shopping days left. *(Cheerfully holding up catalogue.)* You know, you could just phone in an order.

HUMBUG. Why I keep you around is beyond me! I've got to do something to stop "Mr. Nicholas."

HOLLY. Stop Santa?!

HUMBUG. That's right. Stop that cheerful old man with the beard and the red suit. Stop the "ho, ho, ho," the

"Merry Christmas," the colored lights, the good feelings, the cheer. Bah Humbug!

HOLLY. Huh. I kind of like Christmas.

HUMBUG. Knock it off! When I found you last December in the toy department at Macy's, you were sick of Christmas!

HOLLY. Well, that's true…

HUMBUG. First we'll get rid of Santa and then we'll go from there.

HOLLY. *Get rid* of Santa? Look. I don't want to be part of a—a hostile takeover.

HUMBUG *(pacing)*. We're just going to send him on a little vacation—until *January first!*

HOLLY *(cheerfully)*. Oh, okay, a vacation. Somewhere warm? Hawaii? Bora-Bora? Christmas Island?

HUMBUG. Somewhere close.

HOLLY. Greenland?

HUMBUG. We're going to bring him *right here.*

HOLLY *(shocked)*. You mean, we're going to keep Santa here against his will?! *(HUMBUG nods.)* Put on your thinking cap, Mr. Humbug. Every law enforcement officer in the *world* would be after us if Santa's missing.

HUMBUG. And that, Miss Holly Wreath, is where you come in.

HOLLY *(suspicious)*. Where do I come in?

HUMBUG. You go into Santa's office and you take over. You screen his calls. You answer his letters. You make excuses.

HOLLY. I do? How do I do that?

HUMBUG. You become his *secretary.*

HOLLY. Santa's secretary?

HUMBUG. You'll say, "I'm sorry. He's not in the office."
     It'll take 'em months to figure out— *He ain't in the of-*
     fice! And with Santa out of the way—
HOLLY. What? What?!
HUMBUG. You'll see.

*(Lights down on HUMBUG's house and up on the North
Pole. MRS. CLAUS is rehearsing the TREE while
CANDY CANE and ORANGE and PURPLE GUM-
DROPS look on. FRUITCAKE, standing by snow cone
cart, watches.)*

MRS. CLAUS. Now dear, you are a beautiful, green tree in
     the forest, longing for a home—ready to be decorated
     and loved. You want to look your best. Stand straight
     and tall! Reach your arms to the sky. Sway in the gentle
     wind. Beautiful! And then it begins to snow. *(MRS.
     CLAUS calls offstage when SNOWFLAKE does not en-
     ter.)* It begins to *snow! Snowflake!* You're on!

*(SNOWFLAKE skates on, racing across the stage and
off.)*

MRS. CLAUS *(cont'd)*. Oh, dear, not like a blizzard. You
     must skate around the tree as if it's softly snowing.

*(SNOWFLAKE skates back on. MRS. CLAUS directs
TREE and SNOWFLAKE apart as HOLLY, unnoticed,
enters and goes to FRUITCAKE.)*

HOLLY. Have you seen him?
FRUITCAKE. Who?

HOLLY. Santa!

FRUITCAKE. Uh, no. I've followed his trail all day and I keep missing him. I feel like a kid on Christmas morning.

HOLLY. Never mind. Humbug's got a plan. Give this note to Mrs. Claus.

FRUITCAKE *(trying to get it right)*. Mrs. Claus…

HOLLY. Tell her it's for Santa.

FRUITCAKE. Santa…

HOLLY. Say it's from Doctor Green.

FRUITCAKE. Doctor Green…

HOLLY. Got it, Fruitcake?

FRUITCAKE. To Mrs. Claus, for Santa, from Green.

HOLLY. Check.

FRUITCAKE. But what does it say?

HOLLY. "Come to the barn and see the new baby reindeer."

FRUITCAKE. And Humbug will be waiting for him?

HOLLY. That's right, Fruitcake. We're going to have company for Christmas!

FRUITCAKE. Who is it?

HOLLY *(exasperated)*. Santa!!! *(HOLLY crosses to leave.)*

FRUITCAKE. Where are you going?

HOLLY. I'll be at Santa's office.

FRUITCAKE. Oh, yeah?

HOLLY. I'm his new secretary.

FRUITCAKE. You, Holly? You can't even type.

HOLLY *(irritated)*. Just give the note to Mrs. Claus! *(HOLLY exits.)*

MRS. CLAUS. Very nice. Very nice. You may take a little break, children, and go to the barn and see the new baby reindeer!

(CHILDREN exit excitedly. RED enters.)

RED *(to FRUITCAKE)*. I'll have a strawberry snow cone.

FRUITCAKE. Coming right up. Oh, Mrs. Claus. I didn't want to disturb your rehearsal. Doctor Green gave me this note for Santa. Could you give it to him?

MRS. CLAUS. Why, of course. Aren't you new to the North Pole? *(FRUITCAKE nods.)* How nice. What's your name, dear?

FRUITCAKE. Name? Uh...uh, *Cone*, uh, Claude [or Claudia] Cone.

MRS. CLAUS. Well, Claude, I'm going to send you one of my special fruitcakes this Christmas. Would you like that?

FRUITCAKE *(trying to appear excited)*. Oh, yes, ma'am.

MRS. CLAUS. And I'll give this note to Santa. Thank you, Claude. *(MRS. CLAUS exits.)*

RED. Tell me...Claude. It is...Claude, isn't it?

FRUITCAKE. Yeah, Claude. Claude...uh, Cone. *(FRUIT-CAKE hands RED a snow cone.)*

RED. Claude Cone. Now that's a coincidence. Snow *cone*...Claude *Cone*...very catchy. Well, check you later... *(He crosses to go, remarking to himself.)* Something doesn't smell right here and it ain't the reindeer. *(RED exits, ruminating.)*

FRUITCAKE. Phew! That was a close one. Good thing I can think on my feet.

(Lights down on North Pole. Dogs bark in blackout. Lights up on HUMBUG in dogsled, half offstage. A large, struggling "bundle" is in back of sled.)

HUMBUG *(talking to "bundle")*. And now, Mr. S. Claus, we're going on a little ride—to my place. You'll relax, free from the hustle bustle, settle your brain and have a long winter's nap.

(FRUITCAKE runs in breathlessly.)

FRUITCAKE. Sorry I'm late, boss. What you got in the sack? *(Excitedly.)* Toys?!

HUMBUG. *Santa*, you fruitcake! Now, we'll see what happens to the happy holidays without that colorful, jolly, old elf.

FRUITCAKE. What *will* happen, boss?

HUMBUG. They'll lose their *spirit*, Fruitcake—every elf—every man, woman and child. And soon the cookies, the glass ornaments, the cheery faces will be but a dim, faded, *colorless* memory. *(The "bundle" struggles in muffled protest.)*

HUMBUG *(cont'd., to "bundle")*. And at last, I, Mr. Nicholas, am going to celebrate a Happy New Year! Hold on, Fruitcake! *(HUMBUG grabs the reins.)* Mush! Mush!

(Dogs bark and sled moves offstage as the lights fade. Lights up on CITIZENS of the North Pole [RED, MRS. CLAUS, DOCTOR GREEN, ELVES, TREE, SNOWFLAKE, CANDY CANE, ORANGE and PURPLE GUMDROPS]. ALL face ELDER ELF #2 who is standing on a raised podium tapping a microphone which cuts off and on.)

ELDER ELF #2. Is this working? Can you hear me? Oh, dear, perhaps this will do it. *(ELDER ELF #2 plugs mike into cord tightly.)* Testing, testing…4 calling birds, 3 french hens, 2 turtle doves…testing. Ah, yes. That's better. I am very honored to be here today. Our colorful community is growing and we are here to welcome a new business to Evergreen Street. A new business, which will delight everyone, but will bring special joy to the children of our city. We welcome the North Pole Pet Shop! *(CITIZENS applaud.)* And now to cut the ribbon and open the doors of the North Pole Pet Shop—the leading citizen of our colorful city—Santa Claus! *(Loud applause but SANTA doesn't enter.)* And now, ladies and gentlemen, that jolly old elf himself—St. Nicholas!

(CITIZENS applaud but still—no SANTA. CITIZENS look around,confused and talking.)

RED *(talking above the crowd)*. Has anyone here seen Santa Claus?

(CITIZENS answer "No," and question one another.)

ELDER ELF #2. Well, this is very unexpected. Santa told me in July he would be here. And he never misses an appointment.
TOY TESTER ELF #1. This has never happened before!
ELDER ELF #1. Stood up by Santa? It's unbelievable!
ELDER ELF #2. As a matter of fact, I haven't seen Santa in weeks.
RED. Has anyone seen Santa lately?
ELF GIRL #1. He sent me a birthday card last week.

RED. But did you see him?

ELF GIRL #1. Well, no...

PURPLE & ORANGE GUMDROPS. We went trick or treating at his house.

CANDY CANE. But only Mrs. Claus was home.

RED. I see...

TOY TESTER ELF #3. Santa sent us a mushroom pie for Thanksgiving when our gnome relatives arrived from Norway.

RED. But *none* of you actually saw him?

(They ALL shake their heads and answer, "No.")

ELDER ELF #1. Oh, dear, it's December first and Santa is missing!

RED. Let's not jump to conclusions. First I want to talk to Mrs. Claus. Why don't we all get back to work.

TOY TESTER ELF #2. Mrs. Claus is over by the pet shop.

(RED goes to pet shop as CITIZENS, except MRS. CLAUS, ELDER ELVES #1 and #2 and DOCTOR GREEN, exit.)

RED. Ah, Mrs. Claus, I wonder if I might have a few words with you?

MRS. CLAUS. Well, of course, Detective Mistletoe. Oh, the North Pole Pet Shop has the cutest animals—bunnies and mice and kittens. And iguanas and snakes and—

RED. Excuse me, Mrs. Claus, have you seen Santa?

MRS. CLAUS. Seen Santa? Well, I'm sure he's around somewhere. Let me think. When was the last time I saw him? You see, this time of year we never see much of each other. With my baking and rehearsals. His lists—he's checking them twice, finding out who's naughty and—well, you know, so many details—waxing the sleigh, choosing which reindeer—

RED *(interrupting)*. Yes, but when did you last *see* Santa?

MRS. CLAUS. Oh, yes, well it must have been last Tuesday. I'm sure that's right because I always make pot roast on Tuesday and you know how Santa loves my pot roast.

RED. You do make wonderful pot roast, Mrs. Claus.

MRS. CLAUS. Thank you, Detective Mistletoe. Oh, but now—now I remember—his secretary called.

RED. His secretary?

MRS. CLAUS. Yes. He hired a *secretary*. You know, with the volume of children these days, he felt he needed help. And she called and said Santa wouldn't be home for dinner because he had an E.E.A. meeting.

ELDER ELF #1. There was an Elf Elders Association meeting last Tuesday.

ELDER ELF #2. But Santa wasn't there.

MRS. CLAUS. Oh, dear, oh, my. Oh, now that reminds me. She called a few days before *that* and said there was an emergency meeting at the Reindeer Lodge. I remember because that was sturgeon casserole night.

RED. *Was* there an emergency at the Reindeer Lodge?

DOCTOR GREEN. An emergency? No. We just played pinochle and dominoes. I'm the president of the Reindeer Lodge. There was no emergency.

(DOCTOR GREEN and ELDER ELVES #1 and #2 exit, shaking their heads.)

MRS. CLAUS. Now that I think about it, don't you think it's strange Santa hasn't come for a home-cooked meal in weeks?

RED. I think it's *very* strange, Mrs. Claus. And I'm headed over to his office to have a little chat with Santa's new secretary.

MRS. CLAUS. That's a good idea, Detective Mistletoe. And why don't you come over later for some cocoa and cookies?

RED. I'll be in touch.

(RED exits. MRS. CLAUS mulls over the situation as PURPLE GUMDROP runs on chased by ORANGE GUMDROP. They circle MRS. CLAUS who, becoming dizzy, grabs each by the hand and ALL exit together. Lights down on the North Pole and up on SANTA's office. HOLLY sits at desk, reading a magazine. The phone rings. HOLLY answers it.)

HOLLY. No. No. No. No. No!

(She hangs up phone. RED enters.)

HOLLY *(cont'd)*. May I help you?

RED. I'd like to see Santa Claus.

HOLLY. He's not in. *(She resumes reading.)*

RED. No?

HOLLY. No. He's a busy man.

RED. I'd like to make an appointment.

HOLLY *(looking at appointment book)*. Why, look at this. He's all booked up. I could take your name and put you on the waiting list.

RED. The name's Red. Red Mistletoe.

HOLLY *(reading magazine)*. We'll call you if we get a cancellation.

RED. You're new around here.

HOLLY. I'm a temp—a permanent temp. I just relocated from, uh—

RED. North of the South Pole?

HOLLY *(confused)*. Uh, yeah…

RED. And you are Miss…?

HOLLY. Wreath. Holly Wreath.

RED. Well, Miss Wreath, a lot of people are looking for Santa but they're not seeing him.

HOLLY *(sarcastically)*. Isn't that the way it always is.

RED. You have a real sense of humor, Miss Wreath.

HOLLY. Thank you, Mr. Mistletoe.

RED. That's *Detective*. Detective Red Mistletoe.

HOLLY *(nervously)*. Detective? Oh, oh, oh—

RED. Just one more thing, Miss Wreath.

HOLLY *(voice shaking)*. Yes…Detective…Mistletoe…

RED. You've got nice hair. And I know my redheads. *(He starts to go.)* Oh, Miss Wreath. One more thing. Just curious. You're from the South Pole, right?

HOLLY. Uh, that's right.

RED. Well, down at the South Pole—I was just wondering—you got a lot of polar bears down there?

HOLLY. Polar bears?

RED. You know—the big bears with the white fur.

HOLLY. Polar bears. Yeah. We got polar bears by the hundreds. By the thousands!

RED. I was just curious. *(He writes in small notebook.)* Well, see you around.

(RED exits. HOLLY grabs phone and frantically dials. Lights up on HUMBUG's house.)

HUMBUG *(answering phone)*. Yeah?

HOLLY *(hysterical)*. Humbug! They're on to us. I told you so. Why I ever let you talk me into this—

HUMBUG. Calm down! What are you chattering about?

HOLLY. He was here in the office! Asking questions!

HUMBUG. Who?

HOLLY. That detective! Red Mistletoe!

HUMBUG. Relax. We're right on schedule. They don't know anything. It's already starting to work. We'll break their spirit all right. Powder your nose and sit tight.

HOLLY *(doubtfully)*. Okay, Humbug. Okay…

(HUMBUG and HOLLY hang up. Lights down on HUMBUG's house. HOLLY opens purse and puts on lipstick which is black.)

HOLLY *(looking in mirror)*. Hey, what's with this lipstick? This isn't "Cherry Berry Red"!

(HOLLY, alarmed, looks in the mirror as lights fade on SANTA's office. RED appears in spotlight.)

RED. At last, it was December and that's usually the happiest time at the North Pole with Christmas just around the corner. Good will toward men, that's our specialty. But somehow no one was in the spirit.

(Lights reveal ELF GIRL #3 who storms on followed by ELF GIRLS #1 and #2.)

ELF GIRL #3. That's it. I'll never speak to him again.

ELF GIRL #2. What happened?

ELF GIRL #1. You were such a cute couple.

ELF GIRL #3. Oh, yeah? Well, old "*blue* eyes" started hanging out at the Barbie assembly line. And you know why!

ELF GIRL #1 and #2. It couldn't be!

ELF GIRL #3 *(breaking down)*. I hope they're happy together, assembling Barbie's Dream Home and RV and Soda Shop! *(ELF GIRL #3 runs off, crying.)*

ELF GIRL #2. I've never seen her like this.

ELF GIRL #1. I'll be glad when Christmas is over! *(ELF GIRL #1 and ELF GIRL #2 exit.)*

RED. And the children—some of them just didn't look the same.

(MRS. CLAUS enters with CANDY CANE and stops to feel forehead.)

MRS. CLAUS *(worried)*. No fever. But you look a bit pale, dear.

CANDY CANE. But I feel fine, Mrs. Claus.

MRS. CLAUS. Well, all right. But it's chicken soup and bed for you right after rehearsal. *(MRS. CLAUS and CANDY CANE exit.)*

RED. And it seemed cold. It *was* cold. Colder than I remember.

(TOY TESTER ELVES enter, carrying toys.)

RED *(cont'd)*. Hey, out to test some toys?

TOY TESTER ELF #1. No. We're going home.

TOY TESTER ELF #2. Too cold.
TOY TESTER ELF #3. No fun.
TOY TESTER ELVES #1, #2 and #3. Bah humbug.

(DOCTOR GREEN rushes on in a pale green coat.)

RED. Hey, Doctor Green, how's that baby reindeer?
DOCTOR GREEN *(holding up bandaged hand)*. The baby
    reindeer? His mother bit me, I've got to see an elf with
    lumbago and I'm catching cold!
RED. Sorry, Doctor. Well, Merry Christmas!
DOCTOR GREEN. Yeah, right.

*(DOCTOR GREEN exits, nursing bandaged hand. RED
continues in spotlight.)*

RED. That's how December was going—cold and misera-
    ble. We're used to the cold—sure—but at the North Pole
    the sun always shines. This December it was gray skies
    every day. Dismal, dull, depressing and everybody had a
    bad case of the "blahs"…just in time for dress rehearsal.

*(Lights up on the North Pole. Street is full of activity.
ELDER ELVES #1 and #2 are directing TOY TESTER
ELVES who hang a large banner which reads, "Santa's
Send-off Celebration, December 24, 6:00 p.m." MRS.
CLAUS, with a tape recorder, is helping ORANGE and
PURPLE GUMDROPS with their costumes. FRUIT-
CAKE is behind snow cone cart. HOLLY and HUMBUG
enter, disguised as elves.)*

HOLLY. How did I get talked into this? I look ridiculous and I'm going to get arrested for impersonating an elf.

HUMBUG. We've got to keep our eyes on the situation— be sure everything's going according to plan. Just wait and see. It's going to be a *colorless* Christmas without Santa.

HOLLY. I don't know what you're up to, Humbug. I just hope your plan doesn't backfire!

MRS. CLAUS (*calling off*). Places, everyone, for the final dress rehearsal for the send-off celebration. Isn't this exciting? Tomorrow's Christmas Eve!

(ORANGE GUMDROP and PURPLE GUMDROP surround MRS. CLAUS.)

ORANGE GUMDROP. Mrs. Claus, Mrs. Claus! Her purple costume's prettier than my orange one.

MRS. CLAUS. Oh, I don't think so. Orange is one of my favorite colors.

PURPLE GUMDROP. My costume's prettier.

ORANGE GUMDROP. Is not!

PURPLE GUMDROP. Is too!

ORANGE GUMDROP. Is not!

PURPLE GUMDROP. Is too!

MRS. CLAUS. Now, now, let's remember the holiday spirit. Wait offstage, Gumdrops, until your turn.

(GUMDROPS exit, arguing.)

MRS. CLAUS (*cont'd., calling off*). Candy Cane, take your place.

(CANDY CANE enters with jingle bells in each hand.)

MRS. CLAUS *(cont'd)*. Keep your jingle bells still, Candy Cane. *(Calling off.)* Now, Snowflake, you skate around the Candy Cane in a big circle.

SNOWFLAKE *(skating on with difficulty)*. Look, Mrs. Claus, look, my skate's wobbly!

MRS. CLAUS. Toy Testers, will you help fix her skate? Candy Cane, will you keep your jingle bells quiet? *(Calling off.)* Tree, here comes your cue.

(MRS. CLAUS starts recorder and holiday music plays. TREE enters. Unable to see well, TREE bumps into SNOWFLAKE and TOY TESTERS.)

MRS. CLAUS *(cont'd)*. Careful! Oh dear! Candy Cane, quiet! We're nearly to your part.

SNOWFLAKE *(tearfully)*. Mrs. Claus, I need a Band-Aid!

MRS. CLAUS *(calling off)*. First aid!

(ELF GIRLS #1, #2 and #3 rush on. ELF GIRL #1 puts Band-Aid on SNOWFLAKE. ELF GIRLS #2 and #3 help TREE up and to its place.)

MRS. CLAUS *(cont'd)*. Snowflake, that's your cue.

(SNOWFLAKE skates around TREE.)

MRS. CLAUS *(cont'd., calling)*. Now the Gumdrops! Where are the Gumdrops? Candy Cane! Quiet!

(SNOWFLAKE crashes into a TREE causing it to fall down, followed by CANDY CANE, GIRL ELVES, TOY TESTER ELVES and ELDER ELVES #1 and #2 in a domino effect. RED enters, wearing a headset.)

RED. Everybody okay here?

MRS. CLAUS. I think so. Oh, dear, what next?!

(ORANGE GUMDROP runs on in a gray costume.)

ORANGE GUMDROP. Mrs. Claus, Mrs. Claus, look what happened to my costume!

MRS. CLAUS. Oh, my! The color's all gone!

ORANGE GUMDROP. I didn't spill anything on it! I promise!

HUMBUG. Isn't this delicious, Holly?

HOLLY. Well—

(PURPLE GUMDROP runs on in dark gray costume.)

PURPLE GUMDROP. Oh, Mrs. Claus, look! I'm not purple anymore!

ORANGE & PURPLE GUMDROPS. What's happening to us?!

MRS. CLAUS. Oh, dear, I don't know.

(The alarmed CITIZENS crowd around the colorless GUMDROPS.)

HUMBUG. Ho! Ho! Ho! It's working. Give me a snow cone, Fruitcake. My favorite flavor—gray!

HOLLY. Humbug, you've gone too far!

HUMBUG. I knew it! Without Santa, Christmas is doomed!

MRS. CLAUS. What are we going to do? Tomorrow's Christmas Eve!

RED. This looks like a dress rehearsal for disaster.

MRS. CLAUS. If only Santa were here, he'd know what to do. But Santa—Santa—We can't find *Santa!*

(Blackout.)

END OF ACT I

ACT II

(Spotlight shines down on empty stage. Voice of RED.)

VOICE (RED). The mood was chilly at the North Pole. We were colorless, depressed. Christmas was starting to look like a bad movie—and I was in it. A dismal version of *Santablanca*. I was wondering if I'd ever say those words, "Play It Again, Santa." Where was he? The North Pole was *down* and *I was blue*. Well, actually I was gray—

(RED steps into spotlight. His costume is colorless as in a black-and-white movie. All CHARACTERS and sets will be black and white until SANTA's entrance.)

RED *(cont'd)*. Look at me—a shadow of my former self. It was Christmas Eve and time was running out. I was ready to throw in the towel and then it hit me. *The kids!* The kids of the world need Christmas. They deserve it! A real Christmas—a colorful Christmas—and *Santa*, too! I was so mad my face turned red. Well, it felt like it turned red. I vowed to get to the bottom of this mystery. I wanted some answers in black and white.

(RED exits. Lights up on the North Pole. Evergreen Street is colorless. The "Santa Send-off Celebration" banner is black and white. "We Wish You a Merry Christmas" plays slowly and discordantly. BLACK AND WHITE CHARACTERS [ELDER ELVES #1 and #2, PURPLE and ORANGE GUMDROPS, SNOWFLAKE, TREE and CANDY CANE] slowly load sleigh.)

PURPLE & ORANGE GUMDROPS *(sadly)*. Do you think the children will like these toys with the color all gone?

SNOWFLAKE. I don't think so. Can you imagine? New toys under the tree—and they're all gray!

TREE. Who says they'll ever be delivered?

CANDY CANE. That's right. We might as well go home and eat our supper.

PURPLE & ORANGE GUMDROPS *(sadly)*. Our *gray* supper.

ELDER ELF #2. Now let's not get discouraged. I'm sure Santa will be here.

ELDER ELF #1 *(holding a large box)*. Could you give me a hand? Oh, my back!

(ELDER ELF #2 rushes to help ELDER ELF #1. FRUIT-CAKE enters as VENDOR.)

FRUITCAKE. Snow cones! Snow cones!

PURPLE & ORANGE GUMDROPS. No, thanks…

(DOCTOR GREEN hurries past.)

ELDER ELF #2. Hello, Doctor Green, how are the reindeer?

DOCTOR GREEN. Rudolph's nose looks like a headlight! What are we going to do?!

(DOCTOR GREEN rushes off as MRS. CLAUS enters with a burned pan of cookies. RED enters from another direction.)

MRS. CLAUS. I can't believe it! I've never burned a batch of cookies in my life. My nerves are in a tangle. *(Noticing RED.)* Oh, Detective Mistletoe, I'm so glad you're here. Have you ever seen anything like it? Not a blush of color anywhere. Not a hint of a hue.

RED. It's unbelievable, Mrs. Claus.

MRS. CLAUS. And no Santa anywhere.

RED. There's still time 'til Christmas Eve.

MRS. CLAUS *(indicating CITIZENS loading sleigh)*. Look at them. They still care. Loading the sleigh as if he really will come.

RED. There's still hope. I may be on to something, Mrs. Claus. I want to talk with that snow cone vendor.

(RED starts toward FRUITCAKE but is distracted when HOLLY hurriedly enters, holding a basket covered by a napkin. FRUITCAKE exits nervously before RED reaches him.)

MRS. CLAUS. Oh, there's Santa's secretary. *(Calling to HOLLY.)* Oh, Miss Wreath, Miss Wreath!

(HOLLY nervously goes to MRS. CLAUS. RED listens.)

HOLLY. Yes? What is it? I'm kind of in a hurry.

MRS. CLAUS. Oh, Miss Wreath, about my husband? You haven't heard from my husband, have you?

HOLLY. Your husband?

MRS. CLAUS. Santa. My husband Santa Claus.

HOLLY. Oh, yeah, uh, sorry. No, not a word. Didn't phone—nothing, sorry.

MRS. CLAUS. Oh, dear. Oh, I'm…so worried. *(MRS. CLAUS breaks down crying.)*

HOLLY. Say, Mrs. Claus, I'm sorry about your husband. Oh, oh, sorry. Look, I've got to make a delivery.

MRS. CLAUS. Yes, yes, go along. Thank you, dear.

(HOLLY guiltily exits. MRS. CLAUS cries on RED's shoulder.)

RED. Now, now, don't worry. Everything's going to be all right. I want you to go home and bake some cookies for Santa. Don't burn this batch, okay? You know how Santa loves your cookies.

MRS. CLAUS *(drying her eyes with RED's handkerchief).* All right. He does love my cookies, doesn't he? *(RED starts to follow HOLLY.)* Where are you going, Detective Mistletoe?

RED. Just following a lead, Mrs. Claus. Just following a lead.

(RED exits in the direction of HOLLY. Lights down on North Pole and up on the colorless scene of HUMBUG in his house. He is putting up black-and-white "Happy New Year" decorations.)

HUMBUG *(singing).* I'm dreaming of a black and white
  Christmas… *(He laughs hysterically. He sits in a cozy
  chair and with great charm opens a big black leather
  book and pretends to read.)*
      'Twas the night before Christmas
      And all through the house
      Not a child was happy
      'Cause Humbug's a louse!

      The stockings were hung
      By the chimney with care
      Tomorrow they'll be empty
      But, hey, I don't care!

      The children were nestled
      All snug in their bed
      But Santa's not coming
      Because—HE'S NOT *RED!*

*(He laughs in hysterical delight, blows a party horn,
spins a noisemaker and shouts a wicked "Happy New
Year." FRUITCAKE enters sleepily.)*

FRUITCAKE. I'm glad you woke me up. I can't believe it.
  New Year's Eve already! Talk about a long winter's
  nap!
HUMBUG. It was just a catnap. It's Christmas Eve.
FRUITCAKE. So why were you celebrating New Year's?
HUMBUG. Forget it, Fruitcake! Is Santa secure?
FRUITCAKE. Locked up tight. Holly's in there now.
HUMBUG. Why she has to bring him a home-cooked din-
  ner every night is beyond me. She doesn't even bring
  me a cookie.

FRUITCAKE. Hey, he's Santa Claus.

HUMBUG. Can it, Fruitcake!

FRUITCAKE *(handing a snow cone to HUMBUG)*. How about a snow cone?

(HUMBUG grabs snow cone and dumps it on FRUIT-CAKE's head. HOLLY enters from locked door, carrying basket.)

HUMBUG. Well, how was dinner for "Sir Santa"?

HOLLY *(sadly)*. It's Christmas Eve. He didn't feel like eating.

HUMBUG. Aaaaw—

HOLLY *(teary)*. He's so nice. He even asked me what I wanted for Christmas.

HUMBUG. Now don't you get into that sentimental Christmas stuff.

HOLLY *(resentful)*. No, no, not me.

HUMBUG. Get back to the office, Holly.

HOLLY *(bitterly)*. I'm going.

(HOLLY exits HUMBUG's house. RED is outside waiting for her.)

RED. So we meet again, Miss Wreath.

HOLLY *(gasps)*. You followed me!

RED. Just south of the North Pole.

HOLLY. How did you figure it out?

RED. Let's just say a little polar bear told me.

HOLLY. Polar bear? *(Pouring out her confession.)* Oh, all right, I'll tell you everything! He's got Santa in there. He wants to ruin Christmas.

RED. Who?

HOLLY. Bob. Bob Humbug. I knew he shouldn't do it. Christmas is a wonderful holiday—full of peace and joy and love, caring and sharing.

RED. Speaking of sharing—why don't we work together?

HOLLY. To stop Humbug?

RED. That's right.

HOLLY. Nothing would make me happier!

RED. Show me the back door, Miss Wreath.

HOLLY. Call me Holly.

RED. Show me the back door, Holly, and we'll wrap up this case.

HOLLY. And put a big red bow on Christmas!

(RED and HOLLY sneak around to HUMBUG's back door as the lights fade. Lights up on HUMBUG and FRUITCAKE. HUMBUG is pacing.)

HUMBUG. You know something, Fruitcake?

FRUITCAKE. What?

HUMBUG. Something's rotten in Denmark.

FRUITCAKE. Denmark? Isn't that just south of here?

HUMBUG. No, I mean, Holly.

FRUITCAKE. Holly's going to Denmark?

HUMBUG. No, Fruitcake! I mean Holly's up to something. I feel her changing colors like a chameleon. I'm going to follow her.

FRUITCAKE. What about Santa?

HUMBUG. That's *your* job. Follow me!

(An accelerated version of "Jingle Bells" underscores as the chase is on and HUMBUG and FRUITCAKE rush

*off, followed by RED and HOLLY who sneak on and fol-
low them off. Lights cross fade. HUMBUG and FRUIT-
CAKE enter, hurriedly dragging a large sack to center
where it is illuminated by a red light.)*

HUMBUG. You stay here, Fruitcake! And guard the sack!
I'm going to find Miss Wreath!

*(HUMBUG exits as HOLLY enters from another direc-
tion.)*

HOLLY. Hey there, Fruitcake, what's in the sack?
FRUITCAKE. It's *you!* Humbug's looking all over—I
mean—
HOLLY *(tauntingly)*. I'd love to stay around and chat but
I've got some cards to get in the mail. *(HOLLY rushes
off.)*
FRUITCAKE. She's getting away! And that won't make
Humbug happy! But Humbug told me to stay here! And
guard the sack! To stay or go?—stay or go?!

*(Torn, FRUITCAKE runs off after HOLLY as RED
sneaks on and quickly drags off sack. HUMBUG rushes
on, looking here and there for HOLLY, and exits.
HOLLY crosses, followed rapidly by FRUITCAKE.
HUMBUG returns and FRUITCAKE and HUMBUG col-
lide. RED runs on with empty sack, that he holds open
as if to bag HUMBUG and FRUITCAKE, and chases
them off. As lights fade music segues to a bouncy version of "We Wish You a Merry Christmas." Lights up on
North Pole. MRS. CLAUS looks on as ELDER ELVES,*

RED and HOLLY push on Santa's sleigh which holds a large struggling bundle. ALL surround MRS. CLAUS.)

RED *(indicating bundle).* This is from me to you, Mrs. Claus.

MRS. CLAUS. Thank you, Detective Mistletoe, but what is it?

(RED opens the bundle to reveal the guilty HUMBUG and FRUITCAKE.)

MRS. CLAUS *(cont'd., confused).* Oh, how nice…

RED. These two tried to spoil Christmas for everyone.

FRUITCAKE *(pointing at HUMBUG).* It was all his idea!

MRS. CLAUS. Good work, Detective Mistletoe, but can you tell me where Santa is?

RED. Holly?

HOLLY *(tearfully).* Mrs. Claus, your husband is the kindest nicest person I ever met. I'm really, really sorry. And here he is! Santa Claus!

(SANTA enters in his red suit which is the only color on the stage. EVERYONE gasps at SANTA in his red suit.)

SANTA. Merry Christmas! And it's going to be a very Merry Christmas to *all*—thanks to Detective Mistletoe… and Miss Holly Wreath.

MRS. CLAUS. Oh, thank you. Thank you! This is the happiest Christmas Eve of my life! *(SANTA and MRS. CLAUS embrace.)* Tell me, Detective Mistletoe, how did you solve this mystery?

RED. It's all thanks to the polar bear.

SANTA. The polar bear?

RED. Yes, Santa, the polar bear. Both Holly and Fruitcake claimed to have moved from the South Pole to the North Pole. When questioned, they allowed as how the South Pole was swarming with polar bears. Polar bears, Thalarctos maritimus, are inhabitants of the Arctic and are rarely observed over 750 miles south of the Arctic Circle.

SANTA. I see.

RED. You might see a polar bear just south of the *North* Pole, but you'll never see a Thalarctos maritimus just north of the *South* Pole!

SANTA. Red, you're a genius.

RED. No, I'm a detective. And now I have a question. Why, why did you do it, Humbug? Why did you try to wreck the holiday?

HUMBUG. Because I hate Christmas.

MRS. CLAUS. Surely you haven't always felt that way?

HUMBUG. Always!

SANTA. Even when you were a little boy?

HUMBUG *(bitterly)*. Let me tell you about the "happy holiday" at my house. There was no singing, no colored lights bubbling, no gingerbread house, no cookies, candy, punch. And a tree? We didn't have a tree. We had a *twig*. How well I remember that miserable Christmas Eve.

MRS. CLAUS. Oh dear, what happened?

HUMBUG. On that December lst—long ago—I wrote Santa a letter. I still remember it. "Dear Santa—It's not much of a holiday at my house. But it would be the greatest Christmas ever if you wrote me a letter back. I'll be waiting. Your friend, Bob. P.S. And if you could,

I'd really love a red tricycle." Sure I wanted that shiny red tricycle but I needed Santa's letter more...a reason to believe.

RED. So what happened?

HUMBUG. That Christmas Eve I woke up from my happy dream of peddling down the sidewalk with Santa's letter snug in my pocket. I remember it vividly. It was still dark. I went to the twig and looked under the branch. There was nothing—no letter, no red tricycle—*nothing*. I ran away that night and I've been on my own ever since.

MRS. CLAUS. Oh, I'm so sorry, dear.

SANTA *(realizing)*. It's you—*you're* the little boy who ran away!

HUMBUG. What do you mean?

SANTA. If only you'd waited. I have so many houses to visit on Christmas Eve. So many children to remember. When I got to your house, there was no little boy there. And the red tricycle—I've saved it all these years for the little boy with the sad Christmas tree—the little boy who ran away.

(SANTA nods to ELDER ELF #1 who pushes out a new red shiny tricycle with a big bow and a large note.)

SANTA *(cont'd)*. And here it is... Why don't you read the card?

HUMBUG. The card? *(Reading.)* "Dear Bob—Here is your letter. Usually children only ask for *toys* but you asked for something I work all year to bring—the spirit of Christmas. I hope this is your greatest Christmas ever. Your friend, Santa. P.S. Be careful on your new red tricycle." *(Overcome.)* Oh, Santa, I'm so sorry. What can I do? I've ruined Christmas for everyone.

SANTA. No, Humbug, you have the Christmas spirit at last. And that spirit is contagious.

FRUITCAKE. Contagious? You mean it's catching—like a cold.

SANTA. That's right. The joy and spirit of Christmas will spread over the world tonight and I predict a happy, peaceful, *colorful* Christmas morning.

MRS. CLAUS. Santa, dear, it's six o'clock. Time for your send-off.

SANTA. Why, so it is. Let the fun begin!

HUMBUG. But what about the color?

SANTA. Let happiness take its course! It's beginning to brighten up already!

(Surprised, MRS. CLAUS removes her hands from a large pocket in her gray apron. Her gloves are now bright <u>red</u>.)

MRS. CLAUS. Why, it is! Merry Christmas!

(Amazed, ELDER ELF #1, like a magician, pulls a <u>yellow</u> sash from inside sleeve and ties it around waist.)

ELDER ELF #1. Merry Christmas!

(ELDER ELF #2 excitedly unbuttons colorless vest to reveal a <u>blue</u> lining, quickly turning vest inside out and putting it on.)

ELDER ELF #2. Merry Christmas!

(DOCTOR GREEN opens medical bag and is astonished to discover old <u>green</u> coat, putting it on in place of colorless one.)

DOCTOR GREEN. Merry Christmas!

(ELDER ELVES #1 and #2 together reverse FRUITCAKE's apron to reveal <u>orange</u> side.)

FRUITCAKE *(stunned)*. Merry Christmas!

(PURPLE and ORANGE GUMDROPS, SNOWFLAKE, TREE and CANDY CANE, now in colorful costumes, run on. They are followed by GIRL ELVES and TOY TESTER ELVES.)

PURPLE & ORANGE GUMDROPS *(shouting happily)*. Look at us, everybody! We got our color back!

(HUMBUG, needing a handkerchief to wipe his tears, is surprised to find a giant <u>red and green</u> polka dot one in his pocket.)

HUMBUG *(overcome with emotion)*. Oh, oh, oh! Merry Christmas!
SANTA *(reaching in his pocket)*. Oh, Bob, I almost forgot. Here's something else for you. *(SANTA hands BOB a box of crayons.)*
HUMBUG. For me? *Crayons!!!*
MRS. CLAUS. Places, everyone.

(Lights dim as CITIZENS scurry to their places. Light downstage picks up RED. PURPLE and ORANGE GUMDROPS rush to RED and present him with his red hat, exchanging it for the colorless one and returning upstage. HOLLY, having reversed her collar from gray to green, joins RED in light downstage.)

HOLLY. Oh, Detective Mistletoe, I'm so glad you brought me to my senses.

RED. The first moment I saw you, I knew you had a kind heart. And call me…Red.

HOLLY *(full of emotion)*. Okay…*Red.* You saved Christmas…and *me.* Just in the Nick of Time!

RED *(at a loss for words)*. Oh…oh…Holly…*Merry Christmas!* Say, after we send Santa off, would you care to join me for an eggnog?

(RED and HOLLY smile at each other and turn upstage to watch. With holiday music gently underscoring, snow falls softly as "Santa's Send-off Celebration" begins. SNOWFLAKE glides beautifully around TREE, CANDY CANE jingles bells softly and ALL wave "goodbye" as SANTA flies away into the night. Blackout.)

END OF PLAY

DIRECTOR'S NOTES